**A story about how the universe
– something greater than ourselves –
is a loyal friend within in so many ways.**

Dear Readers,

The universe is always there for us. It's there when we wake up in the morning, and it's still there while we are asleep. It's there when we are feeling happy, and it's especially there when we need support. The universe is always with us, which means that we are always held.

The universe inspires us to make and say positive affirmations that support us through life. Affirmations are feel-good words and sweet intentions that we say to ourselves whenever we want. When we say our affirmations, we are simply chatting with the universe… telling it who we are, what we want, and that we are ready for more good things to happen!

The universe is a great listener. It hears everything we say, think, and feel, and it responds to our words, thoughts, and feelings.

The universe wants us to be happy! When we believe in ourselves and our friendship with the universe, it will do everything possible to

# ME and the UNIVERSE

## 14 Affirmations to connect with your inner vastness ...
## For kids (and adults!)

Skye + Fam

help us achieve our dreams. Along with being a great listener, the universe reciprocates by sending us opportunities and blessings to match our vibe.

So, whenever you want the most amazing things to happen, this book invites you to try a simple daily practice of reading 14 affirmations that get you thinking, saying, and feeling  positive vibes.

Does this sound too easy or too silly? Maybe it's supposed to be just that - simple and fun! Just like a best friend, the universe is there for you, inspiring you to be your best self and happy to see you happy.

May embracing the universe reconnect you to your own vastness and wisdom.

In service and gratitude,
Skye+Fam

I am the captain of my own ship,
and the universe is the vast sea on which I sail.

**The energy I put out is the energy I get back, and the universe matches my vibe.**

I mirror the beauty around me,
and the universe reflects
the best version of myself.

**I am unlimited in every way,
and the universe is my playground.**

I am capable of vibrant health and healing,
and the magical rays of the universe
flow through me.

I can overcome anything,
and the strength and wisdom I see
outside of myself is the universe within me.

I choose which thoughts I let in
and which ones I release,
and the universe strengthens my mind.

I give it my all,
and the universe reminds me that
my best is enough.

I can achieve anything I set my mind to,
and the universe gives me everything I need
to make my dreams come true.

I can be anything I choose to be,
and the universe supports me in
becoming more of myself each day.

I have the final say on how I react to life,
and the universe guides me
to stay calm through storms.

I embrace and accept the phases of my life,
and the universe keeps me
grounded in its beauty.

I am kind to myself and to others,
and the universe gives me a boost
when I accept things as they are.

**I stand up for my highest truth,
and the universe has my back.**

# Can You Think Of A Few More?

The universe encourages you to explore your own thoughts and feelings. It invites you to write (or draw) your own positive affirmations.

You can do it! Let's try a few together …

I am _____/

and the universe _____.

I am _____/

and the universe_____.

I am _____/

and the universe_____.

(Just some ideas to get you started: I am BRAVE/LOVED/WORTHY/ENOUGH …
Have some silly fun with this! Remember, the universe is your buddy.)

# About the Author

Skye+Fam ideated their fourth book, Me and the Universe, after a family meditation. A playful collection of 14 soulful ancient affirmations take readers (children and adults) on a journey through the cosmos as it narrates how the universe's vastness, wisdom, and strength is within each of us.

Skye, age 9, and her mom and dad, Payel and Joe Farasat, molded the book through their unique perspectives. The book is illustrated by Payel Farasat. Maya Hooper, a Waldorf twelfth grader, helped edit the images as her high school senior project.

Payel and Joe are Financial Services executives, and certified in coaching, consulting, and mindfulness.

Printed in the USA
CPSIA information can be obtained
at www.ICGtesting.com
LVHW061816221123
764445LV00022BB/64